BUILDING BICYCLE WHEELS

by Robert Wright

Illustrated by Karen Lusebrink

COLLIER BOOKS
Macmillan Publishing Company
New York

COLLIER MACMILLAN PUBLISHERS
London

Macmillan Publishing Company
866 Third Avenue, New York, N.Y. 10022
Collier Macmillan Canada, Inc.

Library of Congress Cataloging in Publication Data
Wright, Robert, 1949–
Building bicycle wheels.
Reprint. Originally published: Mountain View, CA :
Anderson World, c1977.
Includes index.
1. Bicycles—Wheels—Design and construction—
Amateurs' manuals. I. Title.
TL422.W74 1984   629.2'48   84–20070
ISBN 0-02-028260-5

Macmillan books are available at special discounts for
bulk purchases for sales promotions, premiums, fund-raising,
or educational use. Special editions or book excerpts
can also be created to specification. For details, contact:
Special Sales Director
Macmillan Publishing Company
866 Third Avenue
New York, New York 10022

10 9 8 7 6 5 4 3 2

Printed in the United States of America

Contents

Introduction

If you're like me, one of the principal attractions the bicycle offers you is its inherent simplicity, both in design and execution; it's fixable. We ride our machines regularly and we maintain our own machines, repairing them when they need it. By maintaining our own bicycles, we save time and money, and gain the satisfaction of knowing that the job is done right, according to our own standards, at minimal expense, with maximal personal involvement. Our bicycles thus become personal extensions of our selves.

For some reason, however, most of us shy away from repairing or rebuilding our own wheels. When we hit that unexpected pot-hole, hard, and damage a rim, we give up our self-sufficiency. We think, "I'll have to take my bike into the shop and let an expert fix this one. He has all the fancy tools and he knows what he's doing. I don't." Nonsense!

There are no magical secrets to wheelbuilding, although there are rules and opinions. We'll discuss them in depth. But regardless of the materials used (hub, spokes, rim), or the spoking pattern employed (three-cross, two-cross, etc.), the wheelbuilder's technique is basically the same. *Build it tight and true.* The rim, when the wheel is finished, must be a perfect circle. It must spin true; and the spokes must be uniformly tight. That's really all there is to it.

Bicycle wheel building is an art form. It is a labor of love, patience and care, which is one reason why building your own is so satisfying. Its fans and devotees love to relate their theories and opinions, evangelizing esoteric details of the utmost importance. Fine! That's part of the fun; wheel building is a science too. An understanding of basic theory is really necessary for knowing why you're doing something in a particular way. With a bit of theory, you can then design the best wheels for your particular needs! And though there are lots of variables, we'll learn to make some sense out of them.

When it comes to theory, I will do my best to distinguish between fact and opinion. Facts are those things which are most readily verifiable by direct observation and, thus, indisputable ("Spokes in a three-cross wheel are shorter than spokes in a four-cross wheel"), whereas opinions usually arise from empirical evidence, trial and error, and subjective experience ("A three-cross wheel is stiffer than a four-cross wheel"). Inevitably, however, I am bound to err and present some opinions as facts. This is unavoidable, because I have been wrapped up in wheel building and bicycle riding for so long now that many of my opinions have, in my own mind, actually become facts. Let me apologize for this in advance.

Having been an avid cyclist for approximately six years and a professional wheel builder for three, I wrote this book as a result of my own experiences; first rebuilding my own wheels and later, building wheels for friends and customers in the shop where I work. Recently I have become involved in teaching others about wheel building and engaging in discussions (and arguments) about the relative merits of particular wheels under specific circumstances. In my case, however, experience transcends theory. I am going to tell you what I believe is true. My opinions are based on careful study and experience. If I say something is true and it actually is false, please tell me. I am still learning too.

You don't have to understand everything in order to build a first rate wheel. If it holds together and serves you well, it's good, as simple as that. With even just a little mechanical aptitude, a few simple tools and the help of this book, you can build a wheel of the highest integrity, and a wheel that's strong and durable, lightweight and responsive. One that you can ride on and trust. You can do it!

Terms and Definitions

In this chapter we will get acquainted with the terminology of wheels and wheelbuilding. I have tried to present the definitions and descriptions in the most meaningful way, by beginning with the basic components and concepts and building to the more sophisticated techniques.

Wheel. A wheel is the sum of its parts, a total unit consisting of a set of components which are assembled together in a particular way. A wheel consists of a hub, a rim and a set of spokes. Tires, tubes, freewheels, etc. are basically irrelevant to our purposes.

Hub. This is the central portion of the wheel, the part which is attached to the bicycle frame. The hub consists of a shell, an axle set, and a set of loose ball bearings. Conventional bicycle hubs have bearing races of the cup-and-cone design; the cups are pressed into the shell, and the cones are threaded onto the axle. Held in position by a lock-nut, each cone can be adjusted on the axle to obtain optimum bearing clearance between the cup and the cone, thus minimizing rolling friction.

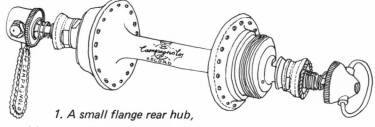

1. A small flange rear hub,
with conventional cup and cone design.

Sealed-bearing hubs are also available, having come into existence only about five years ago. These hubs, manufactured by Hi-E, Phil Wood, and others, require no maintenance or

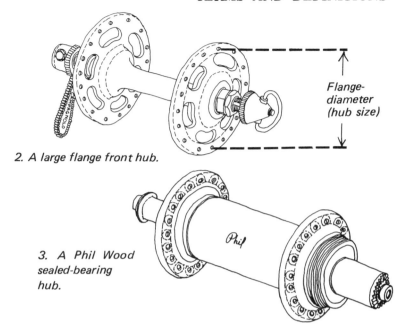

2. A large flange front hub.

Flange-
diameter
(hub size)

3. A Phil Wood
sealed-bearing
hub.

adjustment. The bearings are pressed into the shell and onto the axle, then covered with a neoprene seal to prevent entry of dirt and water while simultaneously keeping the grease in.

At each end of the shell is a flange into which are drilled the holes for the spokes. The size (diameter) of the flange and the number of drillings in the flange are the two important variables which characterize the hub. Hub flanges come in numerous sizes, ranging from about 30 millimeters (one inch equals 25.4 mm, one mm equals 0.039 inch) all the way up to about 100 mm. Most hubs have diameters of 40, 45, 63 or 67 mm. For our purposes we will refer to 40 and 45 mm hubs as small flange hubs, and 63 and 67 mm hubs as large flange hubs. The size of a flange is defined as the distance between two spoke drillings directly across the axle from one another.

Look closely at the drillings on your hub. Often these holes are bevelled or countersunk on one or both sides. The bevel is cut to accommodate the bend of the spoke, not for the head of the spoke to sink into. Hubs that are well-made will have their drillings countersunk, because countersinking reduces the shearing forces which tend to cause spoke breakage.

5

4. *Spoke drillings are usually bevelled, sometimes on one side only, but usually on both sides.*

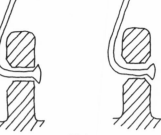

Wrong   *Right*

If your drillings are not countersunk it would be a good idea to buy a small, blunt-tapered hand reamer (available from an auto parts store, a tool shop or even Sears) and bevel your own drillings. Just remove the sharp corner which would tend to cut into the spoke. The drillings need to be bevelled only on the side which accommodates the spoke's bend, so you can get by with bevelling the outside of every other drilling, and bevelling the inside of the drillings which you didn't bevel on the outside.

Look straight across the hub from one end of the axle towards the other end, and notice that the drillings on one flange are exactly staggered, or offset, with respect to the drillings on the other flange. Each drilling projects across the hub to a point midway between two drillings on the opposite flange. The spoke which goes from this particular drilling will connect to the rim next to a spoke from one of these two offset drillings. Study an existing wheel, if you can, to clarify this in your mind.

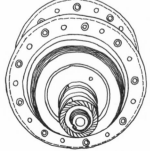

5. *Rear hub viewed from right (freewheel) side. Note counter-sinking of every second drilling and drilling offsets.*

Rim. The rim is the outermost portion of the wheel, the circular hoop upon which the tire is mounted. It is connected to the hub via a set of spokes. Obviously, the rim must have the same number of spoke holes as the hub as spoke drillings in order for them to be compatible as partners. Notice that half the holes are offset (canted) to the right, the other half (every other hole) are offset to the left. This offsetting is done to provide the straightest line possible for the spoke to follow as it connects the hub and rim together. The orientation of the offset holes next to the tire valve hole classifies the rim as either Type A or Type B. This affects the placement of spokes during the lacing process.

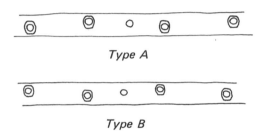

Type A

Type B

6. *Rims viewed from outside edge show center of channel in relation to tire valve hole.*

Rims fall into two broad categories: those intended for use with sew-up tires (tubular rims), and those intended for use with wired-on tires (clincher rims). The tubular design is more efficient than the clincher design, from an engineering viewpoint, and for equal weights, the tubular is the stronger rim. Most clincher rims are much heavier than tubular rims, however, and are not as prone to damage. As a very rough rule of thumb, a rim's strength and durability are proportional to its weight. Tubular rims are made of aluminum alloy, whereas clincher rims come in a steel variety as well as aluminum. The steel rim, being stronger, is less prone to damage; its heaviness, however, does not make for a very lively or responsive wheel and is therefore usually reserved for the most mundane and utilitarian purposes. Most ten-speed bicycles are equipped with aluminum rims (whether tubular or clincher), with 36 holes and a 27-inch diameter.

Rims are further classified according to whether or not they have ferrules, or grommets, in them to reinforce the spoke holes. A ferrule helps to distribute the stress applied by the spoke in a more even and uniform way around the spoke hole, minimizing cracking and lifting of the rim. This is particularly important in tubular rims, because the metal wall is very thin. Most tubular rims are ferruled, therefore, while most clincher rims are not ferruled, with several notable exceptions. Super Champion clincher rims are ferruled (so are some others); Martano tubular rims are not ferruled, and require the use of small washers (provided with the rim) under the spoke nipples (as do several other brands of tubular rims).

The lateral strength of a rim is an important quality which affects the durability of a wheel. Lateral strength is the amount of force applied in a sidewise direction required to deform the rim laterally, that is, push it out of plane. Comparing two rims of equal weight and design, the wider rim will be laterally stronger than the narrow rim, and will tolerate more abuse. This fact makes the Super Champion Arc-en-Ciel a better choice for use in the rear than the Super Champion Record du Monde. See Rim Table, Appendix C.

Spokes. The spokes are the magical wires that hold the wheel together, that are called upon to perform miraculous feats of strength, undergoing incredible stress and strain. A spoke is actually a threaded stud, which is connected to the hub by its head and connected to the rim by a threaded nipple (nut) which

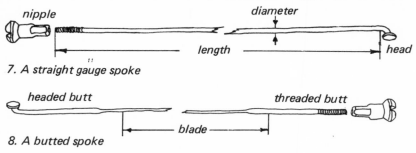

7. A straight gauge spoke

8. A butted spoke

passes through the rim. The nipple is usually made of brass, while the spoke itself is commonly made of zinc-plated, medium carbon steel or "stainless steel." Spokes can either be straight gauge (sometimes called plain gauge), which means that the spoke is of uniform thickness or diameter, or they can be butted (sometimes referred to as "swaged"), which means that they are thinner in the blade and thicker at the ends (butts) where the stresses are concentrated.

Spoke sizes are specified according to length and diameter. The length of a spoke is the distance "from the bend to the end," and is usually expressed in millimeters or inches. Measuring from the bend allows you to hook the spoke over the end of a ruler and read its length directly. The diameter of the spoke is the cross-sectional size of the spoke itself, traditionally expressed as "gauge," from Standard Wire Gauge, but often as inches and, more commonly now, as millimeters. See the Conversion Chart, Appendix E. The most common spokes are 1.8 mm (15 ga., 0.072") and 2.0 mm (14 ga., 0.080") plain, 15/17/15 ga. (1.8/1.4/1.8 mm) butted, and 14/16/14 ga. (2.0/1.6/2.0 mm) butted. Notice that a smaller gauge number is actually a larger diameter. In cases where three diameters are specified, the first and last refer to the butts, the second refers to the blade.

For a given diameter, the strongest spokes commonly available are made of zinc-plated medium-carbon steel, usually called "Rustless" spokes. These are also the least expensive. They will, however, eventually turn dull and lose their lustre. This makes them undesirable from a purely cosmetic standpoint. Chrome-plating carbon steel spokes makes them appealing to the eye, but makes them brittle and weak; they are OK for the show bike, but no good for the serious cyclist. "Stainless

9. Common spoke wrenches

steel" (actually a nickel-chromium alloy) spokes stay pretty, cost about three times as much as rustless spokes, but are weaker (more brittle), tending to break when you'd least expect it. For a typical carbon steel (rustless) spoke with a tensile strength of 20,000 lb/sq in., a stainless steel spoke of the same size has a tensile strength of about 15,000 lb/sq in.

BUILDING BICYCLE WHEELS

Spoke wrench. A tool used to turn the spoke nipples, whether to tighten or loosen the spoke. It is basically a small, open-end style wrench, and is available as either a single-size variety or as a combination, one-wrench-fits-all-sizes variety. I find that the single-size variety is much easier to use and generally fits the nipples better. (Wrenches and nipples come in various sizes.) Be sure the wrench you use fits *your* nipples!

Freewheel remover. Another tool you are likely to need is a freewheel remover. These come in various shapes, sizes and brands, designed to be used with the various makes of

  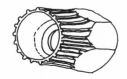

10. Common freewheel removers.

freewheels. Be sure to get the one that fits your hub and freewheel! Removers are usually not interchangeable with one another. If you have one of the old type Shimano freewheels (the kind with the spline, not the two-pronged Dura-Ace) on a Phil Wood hub, don't bother to buy a freewheel remover yet. You will have to take your freewheel apart just to get it off, because no remover alone will take it off. Replace it with a SunTour or Regina, or similar freewheel, and then buy the appropriate remover. Always use it very carefully.

Jig. A jig, or truing stand, is a tool which you probably do not have. Good ones are expensive to buy. They are handy but they are not essential to building good wheels.

You can use the caliper brakes on your bicycles just as well, with proper adjustment. Simply hang up your bicycle so that whichever wheel needs truing is off the floor, and your bike is more or less upright. Position your brake blocks so that you can lay some flat object across the top of them to serve as a roundness reference, and adjust them (with the cable or barrel adjuster) so that they give good side-to-side reference. That's all you need.

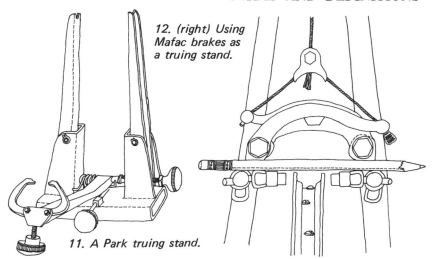

12. (right) Using Mafac brakes as a truing stand.

11. A Park truing stand.

Spoking Pattern. This refers to the orientation of a spoke in the wheel, relative to the other spokes in the wheel. Most wheels are built either three-cross (abbreviated 3X) or four-cross (4X). Three-cross means that any given spoke crosses three

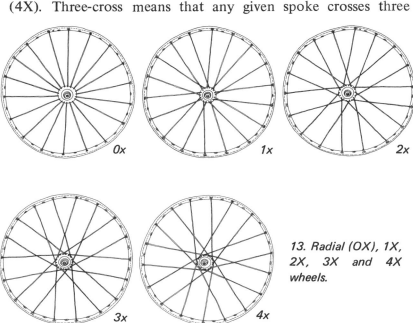

13. Radial (OX), 1X, 2X, 3X and 4X wheels.

11

BUILDING BICYCLE WHEELS

spokes as it travels from hub to rim; similarly a 4X spoke crosses four spokes. It is possible to build a wheel using a radial (0X) pattern, 1X and 2X, in addition to 3X and 4X patterns.

Spokes can be further described as either pulling spokes or as static spokes, depending on their orientation in the wheel. Pulling spokes are sometimes called trailing spokes; static spokes are sometimes called leading spokes. Pulling spokes are said to "radiate backwards" in the wheel; that is to say, they leave the hub and aim towards the rim in a direction which is backwards relative to the forward motion of the wheel. Similarly, static spokes "radiate forward" in the wheel.

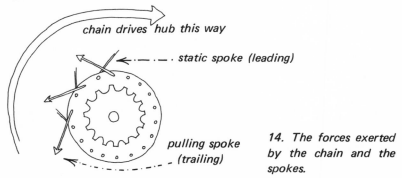

14. The forces exerted by the chain and the spokes.

For clarification, look at a rear wheel from the right side (the freewheel is closest to you). Forward motion of the wheel is from left to right. All the spokes which leave the flanges of the hub in a counterclockwise (left-hand) direction are pulling spokes. The remaining spokes, all of which leave the flanges in a clockwise (right-hand) direction, are static spokes. During times of acceleration, the pulling spokes experience increased tension. This happens whenever you step on the pedals or apply the brakes, but the effect is most pronounced on the right side of the rear wheel (next to the freewheel) whenever a rider starts a sprint, or climbs a hill, applying considerable torque to the rear hub.

Additionally, spoking patterns can be either symmetrical or asymmetrical.

Study the drawings as you contemplate the definitions. A symmetrical wheel is one whose spokes radiate away from one flange in a mirror-image of the way the spokes leave the other

12

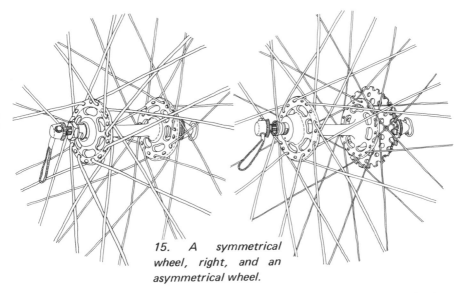

15. *A symmetrical wheel, right, and an asymmetrical wheel.*

flange. By contrast, an asymmetrical wheel has identical spoke/flange orientations as you view it directly. Stated another way, in a symmetrical wheel, all the pulling (trailing) spokes leave the flanges from either the outside *or* the inside, but not both ways; in an asymmetrical wheel, however, the pulling spokes leave one flange from the outside, the pulling spokes leave the other flange from the inside.

Keep studying the drawings as you think about these definitions, and consider what we mean when we say "symmetrical." We're talking about bilateral symmetry. The human body is bilaterally symmetrical. Your right hand is a mirror image of your left hand, certainly not an identical copy as you view it directly. The same is true for your arms, legs, feet, ears, etc. If you cut a vertical plane down the middle (of your body or a symmetrical wheel) you get two pieces, each of which is a mirror image of the other. More or less.

The reason for this discussion is that I believe it's best to build rear wheels symmetrically, with all the pulling spokes leaving the flanges from the outside faces. For further discussion of this topic, see Chapter 4, "Theories and Modifications."

Building. Building a wheel refers to the total process of

putting a wheel together, starting with a set of components and finishing with a wheel which, after mounting a tire, is ready to be ridden. Building, in turn, consists of lacing up the wheel and truing it.

Lacing. Lacing a wheel simply means putting all the spokes in their proper places. Most wheel builders will weave each spoke through the other spokes; in a 3X wheel, for example, each spoke touches the third spoke it crosses as it travels from the hub to the rim. Of course, weaving is impossible in a radial (0X) wheel.

Weaving the spokes enables each spoke to share its workload with another spoke (the one it touches) and results in a somewhat stiffer wheel. A stiffer wheel tends to be more rigid, both up-and-down (radially) and side-to-side (laterally). Stiffness is a quality which is affected by many factors, some of which are cross-pattern, hub flange size and spoke length, spoke diameter, and spoke tension. Tying woven spokes together at their contact points and soldering the joint is one method of increasing the stiffness of a wheel. Tying and soldering two spokes together decreases the effective lengh of the spokes and checks (damps) vibration in the spokes. This is usually done with no. 28 gauge copper wire.

Truing. Truing is the final process of building a wheel. Truing consists of tensioning the spokes and centering the rim, so the spokes are uniformly tight, and the rim forms as perfect a circle as possible. The rim circle must have the hub axle as its center, and the plane of the rim must bisect and be perpendicular to the axle. On a front hub, centering the rim between the locknuts means centering the rim between the hub flanges; on a rear hub, however, centering the rim means positioning it closer to the right-side flange than it is to the left-side flange. This process is usually called dishing the rear wheel.

Dishing. Dishing is done by tensioning or tightening the right-side (freewheel side) spokes more than the left-side spokes. This results in spokes on the freewheel side having a shorter "active length" (distance from the bend to the nipple) than those on the left-hand side. These tighter spokes have a steeper slope (closer to the plane of the rim). Another way of stating this is to say that these tighter (freewheel side) spokes have a smaller bracing angle. Bracing angle is defined as the angle between the plane of the rim (vertical) and the spoke as it moves out to the flange of the hub. See the illustration.

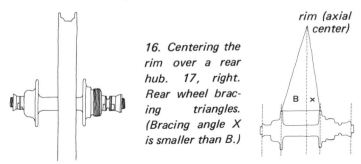

16. Centering the rim over a rear hub. 17, right. Rear wheel bracing triangles. (Bracing angle X is smaller than B.)

Spoke tension. The tension in a spoke is a measure of its tightness. The tighter a spoke is, the harder it pulls on the hub and rim. In other words, the spoke is exerting a force on the hub and the rim, and, of course, the hub and rim are exerting equal but opposite forces on the spoke. Tension (amount of force) is a scalar quantity (a number, signifying magnitude only) but force is a vector quantity (signifying both magnitude and direction). The force which a spoke exerts on the hub and the rim acts in the direction of the spoke, along its line.

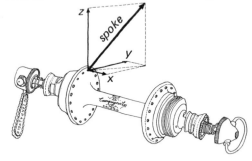

18. Force vector resolution. Z (radial) is always larger than X (lateral). For 2X wheels, Y (tangential) is approximately equal to Z. For 3X and 4X wheels, Y is larger than Z.

Taking any spoke we can resolve its force vector into three mutually perpendicular components. For those of you who have studied some linear algebra, we are setting up a coordinate axes system. Orienting our hub so that its axle is horizontal and such that the spoke under consideration is attached to a drilling located at the top of the flange, our x-, y- and z-axes are, respectively, lateral (axial), tangential, and radial. See the accompanying illustration.

Building Your Wheel

Now we will go through the steps of how to build a wheel. This involves two major processes, namely lacing and truing. To 'lace,' according to Webster, means "to draw together the edges of by or as if by a lace (cord, string, wire) passing through eyelet holes." Lacing a wheel is sometimes called "spoking"; it simply means putting in all the spokes in the right places. Truing, on the other hand, is the finalizing process in which we make the wheel round and tight. Lacing is the easy part, truing is the harder part.

If you can build a good rear wheel, you can certainly build a good front wheel, as a rear wheel takes incredibly more abuse than a front wheel. Therefore, let's concern ourselves with building a rear wheel — for a five- or ten-speed bicycle, since most serious cyclists ride derailleur bicycles. With this basic procedure, you will be able to build any wheel, making appropriate modifications where necessary. The principles are the same.

PREPARATION

Step 1. First, you must analyze your old wheel. Take off your tire, tube and rim strip and remove the freewheel. With a spoke wrench, remove two of your old spokes. Measure the spoke length. Examine your old wheel. Is it three- or four-cross? How many holes are in the rim? Is the rim a clincher or sew-up? Is it made of steel or aluminum alloy? Is there a brand name on it anywhere? It's a good idea to write all of this down for future reference.

Step 2. Look at your hub. Does it have 36 spoke drillings? Check them carefully for countersinking. Were the spokes laced properly when the wheel was built? Check the size of your flanges. Is it a large flange hub or small flange hub? Are you going to build a clincher wheel or a sew-up wheel? Look over the Rim Tables (Appendices C & D). Consider the use to which this wheel will be put, the treatment it is going to receive.

Step 3. You need to buy a new rim and a set of spokes, so now is the time to head for your local bicycle shop. Take your two spokes and your old wheel with you. You might want to take your book and your notes with you too, so you'll have them handy while making your purchases.

Step 4. Buy a rim and a set of spokes which will serve your needs. Get spokes which have nipples with a slot in the end for a screwdriver. Don't hesitate to ask the bike shop people for their opinions, but most likely you will want to build your wheel three-cross (3X). Be sure to get the proper length spokes. If you are building a rear wheel, you can get half your spokes two millimeters shorter than the other half, for use on the freewheel side of the wheel, but this is not critical and may only lead to confusion.

Step 5. Buy a spoke wrench which·fits your spoke nipples, if you do not already have one. You can get either the fifty-cent single-size variety or the seventy-five-cent multi-size wrench which will fit any spoke nipple you're ever likely to encounter. See Spoke Wrench, under Terms and Definitions.

Step 6. Take your supplies home and prepare your working area. The fun is about to begin.

Step 7. Find an old Coke bottle cap or some similar small receptacle. Squirt some oil into it, 3-in-1, SAE 20 or 30, some Sturmey-Archer or Challenge oil. Any oil is fine. This oil is to be used for lubricating the spoke threads.

Step 8. Take out or cut out all your old spokes and throw them away. Keep your old rim if it is a sew-up type, for stretching and aging new tires. Recycle your old clincher rim.

LACING

Step 9. Sit down comfortably. Cross-legged on the floor works pretty well. Assemble your materials around you: hub, rim, spokes, and oil-cap. You might also want a narrow-blade screwdriver. The idea is to have everything within reach. Put down some newspapers so you don't get any oil on the floor!

Step 10. Take your hub and insert one spoke through a drilling on the freewheel side flange. If your hub's drillings are

BUILDING BICYCLE WHEELS

countersunk, pick a drilling which is countersunk on the outside and insert the spoke from the inside to the outside of the flange, so that the bevel (on the outside) accommodates the bend of the spoke. This spoke (and eight more just like it) is going to radiate backwards from the hub out to the rim; name it "Spoke One."

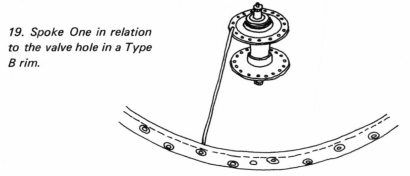

19. Spoke One in relation to the valve hole in a Type B rim.

Step 11. Set down the hub and spoke; pick up the rim. Stand the rim up on the floor and pretend you are stting directly behind your bicycle, so that you are looking at the channel of the rim. Notice how the spoke holes (ferrules) are staggered off-center, alternating left-right-left. Now rotate the rim until you are looking at the tire valve hole. Check to see whether your rim is Type A or Type B. Most rims are Type B.

Step 12. Find the first right (freewheel) side spoke hole which is located forward of the valve hole. In Type A, it is located next to the valve hole; in Type B, it is the second hole forward from the valve hole. Spoke One goes here. Daub a little oil into the nipple threads or onto the spoke threads, insert Spoke One into its proper hole in the rim. Turn the nipple only a turn or two, just enough to attach it.

Step 13. Insert eight more spokes through the freewheel side flange in the hub (heads inside, bends outside), every other drilling, so that you have nine spokes in the hub, evenly spaced. Connect them to the rim, every fourth hole (be sure to oil the threads). Turn the nipples only two turns or so. Keep the spokes loose. Holding the rim stationary, grasp the hub and rotate it forward to make the spokes feel tight. Now your wheel should look like this:

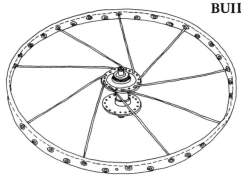

20. The nine right side pulling spokes are in place.

These spokes will be referred to as the "right side pulling spokes."

Step 14. Take another spoke and insert it through an empty drilling on the right side flange, from the outside to the inside (head out, bend in). This spoke will be called the first right side static spoke and will radiate forward in the wheel, from hub to rim.

Step 15. Grasp the hub and twist it forward. Take the loose spoke and radiate it forward out to the rim. Pull it tight and find the spoke hole in the rim which it just reaches. This hole will be offset in the rim channel to the right, of course. For our 3X wheel, this first static spoke will cross three pulling spokes before it reaches the rim; pass it inside of the first two, then weave it outside of the third pulling spoke (they should touch) before you connect it to the rim. Now your wheel should look like this:

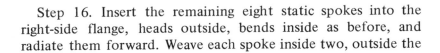

21. The first right side static spoke is connected.

Step 16. Insert the remaining eight static spokes into the right-side flange, heads outside, bends inside as before, and radiate them forward. Weave each spoke inside two, outside the

BUILDING BICYCLE WHEELS

third, and connect it to the rim in its proper hole. Don't forget
to oil the threads, and don't screw the nipples on very far. At
this stage, the lacing is half done.

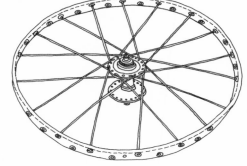

22. The lacing process
is halfway completed.

Now we move to the left-side flange. Basically, we have to
lace it into the rim just like the right-side flange. We will try to
lace it symmetrically. This means that the pulling spokes (which
radiate backward) have their heads on the inside of the flange
and their bands on the outisde of the flange. The countersinking
on the hub must permit this; with some hub and rim
combinations, it can't be done, but these are rare.

Step 17. Hold your wheel so that you are looking across the
hub from right to left, and find Spoke One, which was the first
right side pulling spoke. Sighting across the hub, notice the two
drillings in the left flange which project adjacent to the drilling
through which Spoke One is inserted. Your first left side pulling
spoke will go through one of these two drillings, depending on
whether your rim is Type A or B(see ill. page 7).

If your rim is Type A, insert a spoke through the drilling
which projects ahead of Spoke One's drilling; if your rim is
Type B, insert the spoke through the drilling which projects
behind but adjacent to Spoke One's drilling. Insert the spoke
through the drilling from inside to outside, if the countersinking
allows this; that is, try to have the bend on the outside of the
flange, if possible.

Step 18. Radiate this spoke backward from the hub to the
rim. It will reach approximately to the valve hole. Connect it to
the rim through the first empty hole ahead of (forward from)
the valve hole. If your rim is Type B, this spoke will connect
next to the valve hole; if Type A, it will be one hole removed

from the valve hole. Either way, it ends up adjacent to Spoke One, whether behind it or ahead of it.

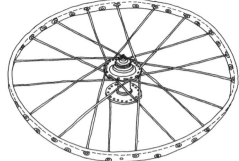

23. The first left side pulling spoke is in place.

Step 19. Now insert spokes through the left flange, from outside to inside. These nine spokes will radiate forward, from hub to rim and will be called the left side static spokes. Start with the two drillings adjacent to the first left side pulling spoke which you just connected and, again, insert through every other drilling to give even spacing around the flange. Be sure to observe the countersinking, if any. Due to interference from the 18 spokes on the right side flange, these nine spokes are the hardest to lace. They would be even harder if we were to lace them after lacing the eight remaining pulling spokes, so we do them now instead. Free these nine spokes from entanglements with the spokes on the other side of the hub and radiate them forward. Be careful not to bend them excessively; you can get them free with careful placement and careful "unweaving" from the spokes already connected. Be gentle and patient!

Step 20. Re-examine the drillings as they project across the hub, from flange to flange, and carefully connect these nine static spokes to the rim in their proper places. They should radiate forward. Also, the spoke which crosses the first left pulling spoke before connecting to the rim should be woven so as to pass outside of (and touch) this first left pulling spoke.

Step 21. Insert the remaining eight left side pulling spokes through the eight remaining empty drillings (heads inside, bends outside), radiate them backwards, and weave each one outside the first two and inside the third static spoke it crosses before connecting to the rim. It should be touching the third spoke. Connect all eight in this manner and the lacing is complete.

21

BUILDING BICYCLE WHEELS

Check your wheel carefully to make sure that all the spokes are woven properly and go to the right places. The valve hole in the rim should be between two groups of four spokes so as to allow convenient space when pumping up the tire.

TRUING

This is the part which requires your utmost care and patience. This is the part where wheelbuilding truly becomes an art. You must get your wheel true and you must get it tight. This process requires caution, because it's possible to over-tighten some spokes before the others are ready. You must work with the wheel as a whole, and tighten each spoke only a little bit, working all around the wheel in a systematic manner. The goal is a wheel whose spokes are optimally and uniformly tight, and whose rim is perfectly round and centered. If you can achieve this, you will have produced a state-of-the-art wheel.

Some people would have you believe that such a wheel can be produced only by a Michelangelo, or a reasonable facsimile at your local bicycle shop. That's simply not so, and you can prove it. You just have to be interested in what's happening and you have to be careful; you have to pay attention to what you're doing and you have to think about it.

My point is, that simply by trying it, you can overcome a fear of the unknown and build a wheel that's as good as anybody's. To tighten your spokes properly and uniformly, you have to do it by feel. Appearance alone is not enough. The best way to tell how tight your spokes are is by how hard it is to turn the nipples. Oiling the threads helps out here, giving you a clearer and more accurate tension signal.

If, at this stage, you have managed to lace up your wheel properly but are too scared to attempt the truing process, then go ahead and take your wheel down to Michelangelo. He will be able to true it for you and you will still have saved the labor cost of lacing the wheel. This is a bail-out of last resort, however.

Step 22. Start slowly. Adjust your hub properly so the axle has no play. Using your fingers or a small screwdriver, carefully tighten each right side nipple about two turns. The oil in the threads will help ease the firction between the spoke and the nipple. Be consistent in the amount you tighten each spoke; that is, tighten each spoke about the same amount.

Think for a moment about this wheel. The hub is designed to accommodate a freewheel on the right hand side of the wheel, between the flange and the fork end (drop-out). Notice that the hub flanges are not centered between the ends of the axle, even though we must true the wheel such that the rim is centered. This means that we will have to dish the wheel by tightening the right-side spokes more than the left-side spokes, in order to bring the rim closer to the right-side flange of the hub. For this reason, we tighten the right-side spokes more and sooner than the lefts. Review 'Dishing' under Terms and Definitions.

Step 23. Carefully tighten each left-side spoke a couple of turns. Right now we are just trying to remove the slack in the spokes, only beginning to tighten them, keeping them about the same length (so that an equal number of threads show below each nipple).

Step 24. Move back to the right side and tighten these spokes again, a turn or two, depending upon how tight they are becoming. As yet, none of the nipples should be very tight.

The object here is to get the slack out of the spokes, to tighten them only equal amounts without exerting any tension on the rim as yet, keeping the spokes uniform. In theory, you should be able to true the wheel without even using a jig, simply by tightening all the right-side spokes an equal number of turns, and by tightening the left-side spokes equally, until the wheel is tight and centered. In practice, however, this does not work because of minor variations in spoke length, shape and location of drillings in the flanges, and ferrule depth in the rim. We have to have some reference points to help us get the wheel true. At this stage, therefore, we put the wheel into some kind of jig.

The simplest jig is your own bicycle, if you have caliper brakes. Simply by putting the wheel into the frame and adjusting the brake into a suitable position you have a good reference. Some people prefer to use the eyeball method only, but I find that allowing for some contact or touch makes it easier to true the wheel, because the touch allows you to pinpoint the exact spots which need adjusting. So set your brake such that the wheel will turn but will touch a brake shoe where it wobbles. This is the flatness reference.

A pencil or other similar straight object laid across the top of the brake shoes will serve as a roundness ("hop") reference to show where the rim needs to be brought in closer toward center.

If, on the other hand, you are able to do so, try to get a hold of a truing stand. To buy one is pretty expensive ($25 and up), and certainly not practical unless you plan to turn pro. But most likely, you can borrow one from a neighborhood bikie. This will make it easier to true up your wheel, and more quickly too. Don't be discouraged if you have to use your bicycle, however, because this too works very well. I do it myself at home.

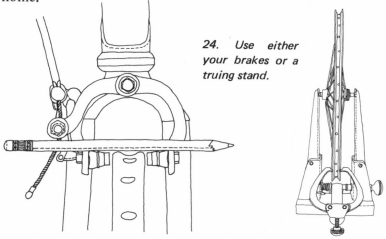

24. Use either your brakes or a truing stand.

Step 25. Put your wheel into your jig. If you are using your bicycle as your jig, hang up the bicycle so that your wheel is suspended off the floor. The easiest way to do this is to tie your saddle up to some overhead object. The only wheel you need to have off the floor is, of course, the one you're building. So the other one can still touch the floor (this helps stabilize the bike). Alternatively, you can simply turn the bicycle upside-down and stand it up on its saddle and handlebars. I find this to be more awkward, however, and prefer to hang up the bike, using an old sew-up tire suspended from a hook above.

Step 26. Adjust your jig so that the reference points are within working distance of the rim, say 1/4-inch or so. Begin tightening the spokes on the right-hand (freewheel) side of the wheel, carefully and uniformly, taking your cues from the jig. Where the rim goes (away from the hub), pull it down; when the rim goes (toward the hub) don't pull on it. Similarly, where the rim moves to the left, pull it to the right; where it moves to the right, leave the spokes alone. Strive to work with the wheel as a whole, as a unit, such that as you adjust either the roundness (up and down) or flatness (side to side), you simultaneously improve the other. Start at the valve-hole each rotation, so you know when you've gone full-circle. Use an alligator clip to keep your place when you drop your spoke wrench.

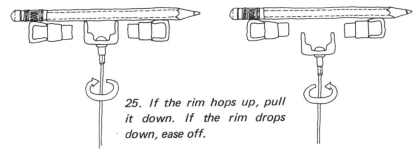

25. If the rim hops up, pull it down. If the rim drops down, ease off.

Step 27. Work on the left-side spokes now, in a manner similar to that used on the right-hand spokes. Slowly and carefully, gradually tighten the spokes to improve the roundness and flatness of the wheel. If some spokes feel tight, don't tighten them more; work with the spokes which feel looser, always taking your cue from the jig. Sometimes you may need to loosen a spoke or two to true the rim and even spoke tension.

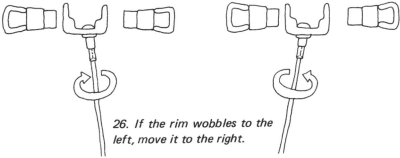

26. If the rim wobbles to the left, move it to the right.

Step 28. When you have achieved some tension in the spokes, stop tightening and remove the wheel from the jig or bicycle.

BUILDING BICYCLE WHEELS

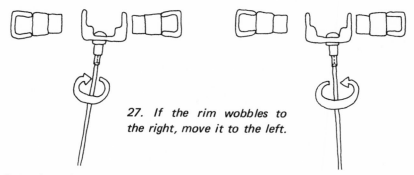

27. If the rim wobbles to the right, move it to the left.

Lay the wheel flat on the floor and kneel down beside it. Hold the rim at the 9 o'clock and 3 o'clock positions and carefully press down with both hands (lean your body weight onto the rim) while the hub is supported on the floor. Lean very gently, carefully, being cautious not to spring the rim. Probably you will hear some creaking and tinkling sounds. This process is known as stressing (sometimes called straining) the wheel. Rotate the wheel about one-eighth of a turn and press again. Continue all the way around the wheel until you don't hear or feel any more sounds. Now turn the wheel over and repeat the process on the other side, rotating about one-eighth turn between each pressing, until you hear no more sounds.

Stressing the wheel repeatedly during the truing process is a very important ingredient to producing a good wheel. When you lean on the wheel in this way, you flex the rim laterally; this increases the tension in some spokes and decreases the tension in others. Increasing the tension helps "bed down" or "seat" the spokes into the hub and rim and helps seat the ferrules into the rim. More importantly, though, is that by taking the load off some of the spokes, you enable them to untwist.

As the spoke's tension increases, so does the friction in the threads between the spoke and nipple. This can result in actually twisting the spoke rather than just tightening the nipple. Oiling the threads prior to assembly helps minimize this twisting. Stressing the wheel eliminates any twist and allows each spoke to assume its actual (true) tension, enabling you to get a clear and factual picture of what's going on in your wheel.

Step 29. Put your wheel back into the jig, but reverse its direction from before. Adjust your reference points to suitable positions and work over the nipples again, striving for roundness and flatness at the same time. Bear in mind that it is harder to get the wheel round than it is to get it flat, so pay closer

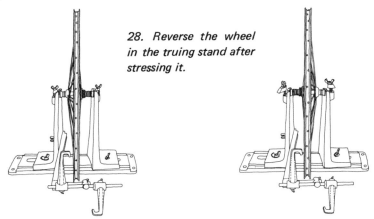

28. *Reverse the wheel in the truing stand after stressing it.*

attention to the roundness. At the same time, however, try to improve both qualities simultaneously whenever you can.

Step 30. Continue the truing process, working with the wheel as a whole. Strive for uniform tension in all the spokes on each side of the wheel; of course, the spokes on the freewheel side

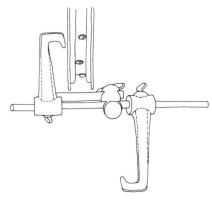

29. *The hooks are the flatness reference; the crossbar is the roundness reference.*

will end up being tighter so that the rim gets centered between the locknuts on the axle. Stress the wheel frequently, and keep turning the wheel around (reversing it) before you replace it into the jig. You turn the wheel around before replacing it into the jig so you continually center the rim over the axle. Clearly, if the rim is perfectly centered between the fork ends (drop-outs) it will be in the same position with respect to the jig references regardless of which way the wheel is set into the jig. You don't need any fancy dishing tools or measurements. Simply continue to tighten, true, stress, and keep reversing the wheel when you replace it in your jig, until your wheel stays true after stressing it.

Step 31. How tight should your spokes be? It's impossible to give a quantitative answer to that, other than to say that they

30. Squeeze a group of four spokes to feel how tight they are.

should be as uniformly tight as you can get them. The rim is the component in your wheel which limits the amount of tension you can apply. If the ferrules start to pull out of the rim or if the (unferruled) rim starts to bulge or crack at the nipples, the spokes are too tight.

Step 31. In finishing the job, you may not need to do anything more. If, however, the rim seam (joint) is rough or uneven, you can file it smooth. Also check carefully to see if any of the spokes are protruding through the nipples. If your wheel is for a sew-up, a small amount of protrusion is OK and will not cause any trouble. However, if your wheel is a clincher type, no spoke protrusions are allowed, because they will eventually puncture your inner tube; they must be filed down flush with the nipple.

Before mounting a sew-up tire on your new rim, clean the mounting surface with a rag and a bit of solvent or kerosene to remove the protective (oily) film from the rim. Let the rim dry thoroughly before applying the rim cement.

You are finished!

Theories and Modifications

I am not an authority in the field of bicycle design, but I have studied some physics and engineering. Even as a professional bicycle mechanic, however, I tend to relate to the machine on a basically intuitive level. Sometimes you feel something that you have trouble explaining, or you realize you believe something that you can't substantiate. The intuitive level sometimes provides us with an insight which is often valid. Then it remains for experiment and experience to test and either verify or disprove this insight.

The way I look at it, wheel building is both an art and a science. Of course, the careful and proper assembly of the components, followed by the tensioning and truing process where the craftsman patiently executes his skill to produce a round, tight and properly centered wheel of the highest structural integrity — this is the art of wheel building. Clearly, two persons, each starting out with an identical set of components, are not going to produce identical wheels. They may be the same design, but not the same wheel.

On the other hand, two persons, each charged with building a wheel to be used in a particular situation or application, are likely to come up with two different designs. Why? Because the science of wheelbuilding has not progressed very far. Accurate knowledge is not widespread. People who know (if they exist) either aren't talking or are being ignored.

I want to get wheelbuilding out of the dark, medieval closets of apprentices and feudal lords. I want to shine some light on the subject. Let's try to find out just exactly what is happening in a wheel, under as many different circumstances as we can, so that we can make intelligent choices when we need to build one.

We will examine various phenomena which occur while a

wheel is being ridden. We will look at some of the many variables which confront the wheel builder. Hopefully, we can describe and understand the static and dynamic activities which a wheel undergoes, how they can be changed and modified, so that you, the wheel builder, will have some clear-cut reasons for building a wheel in a particular way for a particular application.

It's probably obvious to everybody that the rear wheel of a bicycle has to endure more insult and abuse than the front wheel. It carries more weight, and serves as part of the power train, receiving and transmitting torques and forces which the front wheel is spared. The rear wheel is also structurally inferior to the front wheel; in order to accommodate the freewheel, the rear wheel is dished. This results in a wheel whose right-hand spokes are much tighter than its left-hand spokes, thus greatly compromising its lateral stability. As far as analysis and discussion are concerned, therefore, consideration of the rear wheel will suffice to serve our purposes. If we can get a feeling for what is going on in a rear wheel, the front wheel will follow naturally.

PERIODIC STRESS

First, consider the fact that as you are riding down the road, at any given moment you are actually hanging from the uppermost spokes in your wheels. These spokes, which usually go from the sides of the flanges to the top of the rim, are at any given moment tighter than the spokes which go from the top and bottom of the flanges out to the sides of the rim, which, in turn, are tighter than the spokes which go from the sides of the flanges to the bottom of the rim. Top, sides and bottom refer to the relative positions in the wheel as viewed from the side of the bicycle, at any given instant. As the wheel rolls along, the top becomes a side, a side becomes the bottom, the bottom becomes a side, and the remaining side becomes the top. In effect, then, the tightest spokes are moving around the wheel backwards as the wheel rolls forward. With each revolution of the wheel, each spoke in the wheel takes a turn at being tighter, then looser than most of the others. This phenomenon occurs in both the rear and front wheel, and is a natural and unavoidable result of rotation in the gravitational field. Let's call this phenomenon "periodic stress" to emphasize its regularity and predictability.

Periodic stress cannot be eliminated. Gravitational forces on you and your bicycle pull you toward the ground. Since you are sitting on your saddle, or standing on your pedals, or both, this force is transmitted to your frame. The frame is connected to the hubs, which transmit the force through the wheels to the ground. The ground pushes up against your tires, which in turn push against the rims. So the hubs are pushing down, the rims (down at the bottom) are pushing back. The rims are connected to the hubs through the spokes. As the bottom spokes (which are already tight, just by the nature of the bicycle wheel) feel something pushing on them at each end, the top spokes feel something pulling on them at each end! Thus, periodic stress on the spokes is the result of regular, repeated radial deformation of the wheel due to gravity.

Although periodic stress cannot be eliminated, it can and should be minimized. This is done primarily by getting the spokes as tight as practical in the wheel. You can get the spokes only so tight, however: if the ferrules start pulling through the rim, the spokes are too tight! If the holes (unferruled) start to crack, the spokes are too tight. If the rim starts to deform either radially (up-and-down) or laterally (side-to-side), the spoke tensions are not uniform enough. It gets sticky here; experience is not only the best teacher, but the only teacher in this case. It's impossible to tell you how tight to get the spokes.

Why does tightening the spokes minimize periodic stress? Because the tighter the spokes are, within limits, the more the wheel becomes a rigid body, in the physics sense. The tighter the wheel is, the less it can deform. The less it can deform, the less variation in tension will be experienced as it rolls along the ground. The tensions in the spokes will tend to remain more uniform.

Periodic stress can be decreased also by ensuring a good fit between the hub drilling and the spoke. As far as is possible, the spokes should fit snugly in their drillings, and the contact surfaces should be smooth and uniform, both under the head of the spoke and at its bend. A smooth, snug fit minimizes a spoke's flexion at the hub; this flexion (sometimes called

from the other end) and step back on. Spring again. Notice how it's springier? If you try it again at eight, nine and 10 feet, you'll see that your spoke gets progressively springier, the longer it gets. This, too, contributes to the fact that a wheel becomes progressively springier (less stiff) as its spokes get longer.

Now look back at the previous drawing (No. 31) and examine the angles at which the spokes leave the hub. Let's consider what happens in your rear wheel when you step down on the pedals. A torque (twisting force) is exerted on the hub, tending to accelerate the wheel. (Refer to drawing No. 14)

The hub, behaving like a pulley, pulls on the spokes which radiate backward in the wheel. These spokes behave sort of like a rope wrapped around the pulley; that is, the more they are wrapped around the hub, the more effectively they can transmit this torque from the hub to the rim. Stated another way, the more tangential the spoke's orientation is with respect to the hub's flange, the better it can assist in the acceleration of the wheel.

Think of it this way. A torque, or moment of force, in physics, is a force (F) exerted at some distance (lever arm, r) from an axis, tending to twist about the axis (in our case, axle). This happens in your wheels whenever you apply the brakes or whenever you apply power through the pedals. By definition, only the force which is applied perpendicular to the lever arm contributes to the torque. Perpendicular to the lever arm is the

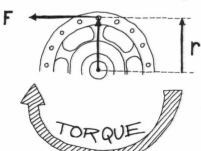

$$T = rF$$

34. The torque equals *r* (hub radius) X F (applied to hub by spoke).

same thing as tangential to the hub so, clearly, a spoke which is more tangentially oriented with respect to the hub will be more in line with the torque's force, and better able to transmit it.

In general, heavier riders will prefer wheels built with more crosses, especially in the rear. Usually 4X is a good idea, at least on the freewheel flange, but 3X is OK, especially if using a large flange hub.

FLANGE SIZE

An extension of our discussion leads us to consider the size of hub flange and its manifestations in the wheel. Comparing two wheels which are alike in everything except flange size, it turns out that the wheel with the smaller flanges will be the springier wheel. Evidently the longer spokes more than make up for their less-tangential orientation. The small flange wheel will also be less stable in a lateral (sideways) direction, because its bracing angles are smaller. Thus, it tends to be the softer, more comfortable, wheel.

The small flange is not as efficient in transmitting torque, however. First, for a given cross pattern, the spokes leave the small flange in a more radial, less tangential direction. Second, the spokes leave the small flange at a smaller distance, r, from the axle. For a given torque in the rear wheel, the pulling spokes will experience a greater tension peak (force) to offset the shorter lever arm, r. Faced with having to make up for less leverage by accepting larger forces, these spokes coming from the small flange are more prone to breakage. This is particularly important on the freewheel flange, where the spokes are tightest, have a particularly small bracing angle due to the rear wheel's dish, and are required to carry most of the torque load during acceleration. For this reason Campagnolo, Phil Wood and Hi-E manufacture a rear hub with a large freewheel flange and a small left flange. Due to the elasticity (non-rigidity) of a hub's shell, the spokes on the freewheel flange bear the greater torque load, so it's best to have them on a large flange.

TENSION PEAKS

"Tension peaks" deserve some discussion. This simply means an increase in the tension of a spoke, to some level, followed by a return to normal. Correspondingly, a "tension drop" means a decrease in spoke tension, followed by a return to normal. Let's look at a couple of examples.

Whenever you accelerate your bicycle you apply a torque to

Seez" or WD-40. Grease does not work well here, due to insufficient penetration into the threads.

Various other methods have been suggested by wheel builders as a means of preventing nipple loosening. I include them for your edification, but I do *not* recommend them myself. Ray Blum recommends degreasing all the threads prior to assembly and then daubing a bit of Loctite onto the threads after truing the wheel. Donald Pensack recommends taking a pair of diagonal wirecutters and lightly crimping the nipples after truing the wheel, presumably to approximate a locknut. Both of these methods make later adjustments difficult; crimping the nipples is downright dangerous because the nipples are seriously weakened.

Lubricating the threads has the additional advantage of decreasing the likelihood of the nipples seizing onto the spokes ("frozen spokes") with the passage of time, particularly with non-stainless spokes.

DISHING THE REAR WHEEL

The strength and integrity of a rear wheel are seriously compromised due to the uneven tensioning required to center the rim over the rear axle and accommodate the conventional five-speed freewheel. For a typical rear wheel, whose locknut to locknut width is about 120 mm, the rim must be pulled about 12 mm closer to the freewheel flange than it is to the left flange. This means that the wheel has about six mm of "dish" (six mm is about 1/4-inch); the rim is six mm to the right of the centerline between the flanges. (Refer to Illust. No. 17.)

Six millimeters may not seem like very much, but to achieve this positioning requires that the spokes on the freewheel side be more than half again as tight as the spokes on the left side. The steeper slope of the shorter (active length) spokes results in a smaller bracing angle on the freewheel side of the wheel. This means that the wheel is laterally less stable, less able to withstand lateral forces acting on the rim from the right (freewheel) side. These forces commonly occur when you are cornering hard to the right, or tromping down hard on the pedals.

Probably you've noticed that most spoke breakages occur in spokes on the rear wheel's freewheel side. Here again, the uneven tensions between right and left side spokes contribute to this. The greater the difference is between right side tension and left side tension, the greater is the proportion of work being done by the right side (tighter) spokes. Carried to the extreme, this means you really are riding on an 18-spoke wheel instead of a 36-spoke wheel. No wonder these spokes break!

Anything you can do to minimize this tension differential will improve the integrity of your rear wheel. Some people like to use a four-speed freewheel, transferring a spacer from the right side of the axle to the left side. This allows you to decrease the dish in the wheel. Another method is simply to spread the rear drop-outs in your frame, install a longer axle in your hub, and increase the spacing on the left side of the axle. A very simple improvement involves using larger diameter plain gauge rustless spokes on the freewheel side of the wheel. More exotic modifications include decreasing the number of spoke crosses on the left side (using shorter spokes) or tying and soldering the spokes on the left side (stiffening up the left side relative to the right side).

Phil Wood, Hi-E and Campognolo manufacture rear hubs which have a large freewheel side flange and a small left side flange. This helps alleviate the difference between the right- and left-side bracing angles. Finding a Campagnolo Hi-lo hub is pretty hard to do, however. I've only seen one in all my experiences with wheels.

Even though six-speed freewheels are beginning to enjoy a newly found favor, especially among racers, their use compounds the problem of excessive dish. Increasing the spacing on the right side of the axle (to accommodate the extra cog) requires moving the rim even farther to the right in order to center it, resulting in spoke tensions approximately twice as great on the right side as on the left!! Six-speed rear wheels are much more prone to trouble than five-speed wheels. You get what you pay for; that extra cog usually costs some headaches. It might be worth it to you, but think about it!

SPECIFIC RECOMMENDATIONS

If I were asked to recommend a type of wheel most universally suited to any application, I would choose a large flange hub, 2.0 mm (14 ga) plain gauge rustless spokes laced 3X

and squeeze the blips together until the smaller one is smooth. Be very careful not to squeeze too far; you don't want to put a dent in the rim, and you can't unsqueeze the rim. Now, to remove the bigger blip, or to remove a blip on one side of the rim only, place a smooth, flat object against the rim on the smooth side. A cone wrench (hub spanner) or a popsicle stick is good for this. Adjust your Vise-Grip and squeeze against the blip and the popsicle stick, carefully, so that you don't squeeze too far but still manage to get the rim's braking surface smooth. Sometimes you can't avoid putting a small dent in the rim, but this certainly is better than having that annoying blip.

The reason for using Vise-Grip pliers is partly that they give you a lot of controlled leverage, but mainly because they are micro-adjustable. Using the threaded adjuster on the end of the handle, you can set the jaws so that you won't squeeze them too far. A Vise-Grip is a specialized tool which you may not already own. Due to its many uses in bicycle maintenance, however, it would certainly be worth getting a pair; the most useful size has jaws about 3/4-inch wide.

Flat spots often accompany a blip. A flat spot occurs when you hit an object so hard that the rim deforms in a radial direction, sometimes resulting in a loose spoke or spokes in the vicinity of the flat spot. There's usually not too much you can do about a flat spot, except tolerate it if it's small. Sometimes you can loosen a spoke or two nearby to help minimize the flat spot. You might even want to try some experiments aimed at improving the flat spot.

Remove the nipples from four or five spokes near the flat spot and move the spokes out of the way. Support the wheel by the hub axle, take a wooden block and a hammer, and place the block against the rim (from the inside) at the flat spot. With the hammer, hit the block *hard*. The object is to restore the smooth curve of the rim. You may have to tolerate a dent in the rim's inside surface.

Or, try placing a piece of two- by four-inch lumber through the wheel where the spokes are removed (as above). The wood piece should be about two feet long. Stand on the board, straddling the wheel, and pull upwards on the wheel, trying to bend out the flat spot. This may work if you're pretty strong.

Either way, it's a pretty crude fix, and may not help much. Do the best you can to restore the wheel to its initial state of trueness (replace and tighten the spokes you removed). If you can't get it into satisfactory condition, just rebuild it with a new rim and be done with it.

Sometimes you may find your wheel has a hop or a wobble. A "hop" is up-and-down (out of round) motion, viewed from the plane of the rim, whereas a "wobble" is side-to-side motion (out of plane). Do the best you can to true the wheel, striving for uniform tension in the spokes, stressing the wheel frequently as you true it. If you encounter any "frozen" spokes, try gripping the spoke near the nipple with your Vise-Grip pliers, as you turn the nipple, to prevent spoke twist. If this doesn't work, cut out the seized-up spokes and replace them. When installing new spokes, don't bend them excessively. Be sure to oil the threads before you screw on the nipples.

Work with the spokes in groups. When pulling down a hop, adjust several spokes in the vicinity of the hop, concentrating on the spokes right at the hop. Similarly with wobbles, concentrate on the spokes closest to the wobble, but spread the load around. Always strive for uniformity of tension among the spokes in the wheel. You may never get the wheel to be as good as new, but you can probably improve it.

It's not always easy to know whether a wheel is worth trying to repair, or whether it should be rebuilt. It's even harder to try to give objective whens and wherefores to help guide you. If your wheel has an atrocious flat spot, forget the old rim and replace it. If your rim has a very abrupt kink (a sharp bend laterally), it is deformed past the point of reasonable repair and should be replaced. Frozen spokes should certainly be replaced. Repeated spoke breakage calls for rebuilding the wheel with a complete new set of spokes. Sometimes you can fix it and sometimes you can't. Experience is the best judge, and acquiring that takes time.

Index